THIS BOOK HAS BEEN PREPARED WITH LOVE BY

FOR MY GRANDCHILD

DATE

IMPORTANT NOTE:
For best results we recommend that you use a fountain pen, a marker or a felt tip to fill in this book.
The pressure of a ball point pen will show through and spoil the following pages.

OTHER BOOKS IN THIS SERIES:
Our Baby's Record Book   My Best Recipes
Our Family Record Book   My Wedding Planner
Golf Score Book   Visitor's Book
Household Record Book   Wedding Guest Book
Our Love Story

Published simultaneously in 1994
by Exley Publications in Great Britain,
and Exley Giftbooks in the USA.

12 11 10 9 8 7 6 5 4 3

Edited by Helen Exley.
The moral right of the author has been asserted.
BORDER ILLUSTRATIONS BY AISLINN ADAMS.

Copyright © Helen Exley 1994.

ISBN 1-85015-516-X

Picture research by P. A. Goldberg and J. M. Clift/Image Select.
Typeset by Delta, Watford.
Printed at Oriental Press, UAE.

Exley Publications Ltd, 16 Chalk Hill, Watford,
Herts WD1 4BN, United Kingdom.
Exley Giftbooks, 232 Madison Avenue, Suite 1206, New York,
NY 10016, USA.

> **IMPORTANT NOTE:**
> For best results we recommend that you
> use a fountain pen, a marker or a felt tip
> to fill in this book. The pressure of a ball
> point pen will show through and spoil
> the following pages.

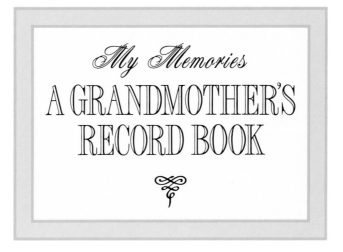

My Memories

A GRANDMOTHER'S RECORD BOOK

EDITED BY

HELEN EXLEY

EXLEY

NEW YORK · WATFORD, UK

INTRODUCTION

This beautiful book is for a grandmother to fill in and pass on to a special grandchild. By recording your memories and telling some of the things that have been important in your life, you will be creating a gift that will actually grow in value – a sense of identity and personal history unique to your own grandchild. The completed book will make a beautiful, lasting record and heirloom to be treasured.

The basic framework enables you to write down your own personal reminiscences, and for you to record the things that are important to you. The suggestions for ways to use each page have been left deliberately loose – there is no right or wrong way to fill it in. Obviously the pattern of individuals' lives varies tremendously – you may have a great deal of information about your childhood or you may have had some particularly exciting adventures that you want to record at length. No one's life will ever fit a standard set of suggested headings!

It's a nice idea to add your own memorabilia – use the blank, double pages for photographs, the words of a well-loved song or poem, a letter or even a piece of fabric from a special dress. You may choose to obscure some of the most irrelevant headings with your own photographs! The more of yourself you put into this book, the greater its value to your grandchild and, perhaps one day, their children too...

HELEN EXLEY

Contents

ME

BIRTH DETAILS, MAIDEN NAME, IMPORTANT FACTS AND DATES.

My Great Grandparents

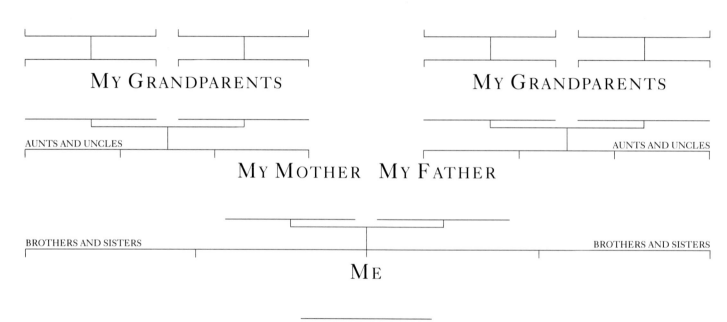

My Grandparents

My Grandparents

AUNTS AND UNCLES

AUNTS AND UNCLES

My Mother   My Father

BROTHERS AND SISTERS

BROTHERS AND SISTERS

Me

GREAT GRANDPARENTS

GRANDPARENTS

GRANDPARENTS

AUNTS AND UNCLES

AUNTS AND UNCLES

MOTHER   FATHER

BROTHERS AND SISTERS

BROTHERS AND SISTERS

YOU

HISTORY OF MY FAMILY

IMPORTANT DETAILS, OCCUPATIONS, BASIC DATES AND KNOWN FACTS.

OUR EARLY FAMILY

SUGGESTIONS: ACHIEVEMENTS, STORIES OR PHOTOGRAPHS.

MEMORIES OF MY GRANDPARENTS

THE WORLD THEN

PAGE 18

YOU COULD WRITE ABOUT HOW EVERYDAY LIFE WAS DIFFERENT –
OR ABOUT HOW YOU LIVED THROUGH HISTORY IN THE MAKING!

MY PARENTS

PAGE 20

FACTS, DATES AND ANY INFORMATION THAT YOU FEEL IS IMPORTANT.

My parents' memories

PAGE 22

SUGGESTIONS: THE STORIES THEY TOLD, THEIR BELIEFS, OR THE WORLD IN THEIR LIFETIME.

My home and family

THESE PAGES CAN BE USED FOR PHOTOGRAPHS, HAPPY MEMORIES OR IMPORTANT FACTS.

My childhood

FACTS, IMPORTANT EVENTS OR MEMORIES.

CHILDHOOD MEMORIES

SUGGESTIONS: SPECIAL FRIENDSHIPS, ADVENTURES, FUN AND GAMES!

SCHOOL-DAYS

YOU COULD WRITE ABOUT YOUR TEACHERS, SUBJECTS AND GAMES OR COMPARE
DISCIPLINES AND VALUES WITH YOUR GRANDCHILD'S SCHOOL.

TEENAGE YEARS

FOR PHOTOGRAPHS, MEMORABILIA, FASHIONS OR PERSONAL CHANGES.

As a young woman

SUGGESTIONS: BELIEFS, ACHIEVEMENTS, EXCITEMENTS, WORK...

ROMANCE

POSSIBLE SUBJECTS COULD INCLUDE – PARTIES, SONGS, BOYFRIENDS, MEETING YOUR LIFE'S GREAT LOVE.

PAGE 37

LOVE AND MARRIAGE
PAGE 38

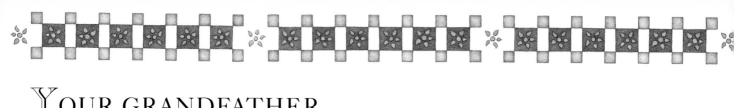

YOUR GRANDFATHER

FOR FACTS, DATES OR IMPORTANT INFORMATION, HIS BELIEFS OR HIS WISHES FOR YOU...

PAGE 41

CREATING A HOME AND A FAMILY

ON BECOMING A MOTHER OR SETTING UP HOME, ANYTHING YOU LIKE ON THOSE EARLY YEARS.

MY LIFE DURING THOSE YEARS

THE PARTS OF MY LIFE THAT WERE NOT BEING A MOTHER –
PERSONAL GROWTH, MY WORK, MY SPECIAL INTERESTS AND HAPPINESS.

MY CHILD – YOUR PARENT

THE EARLY YEARS – SPACE FOR PHOTOGRAPHS, MEMORIES OR IMPORTANT FACTS.

YOUR PARENT'S CHILDHOOD

FOR SCHOOL-DAYS, ACHIEVEMENTS OR FRIENDSHIPS – OR STORIES OF MISCHIEF!

FOR PHOTOGRAPHS, MEMORABILIA, LIKE EARLY DRAWINGS AND LETTERS, OR HAPPY MEMORIES...

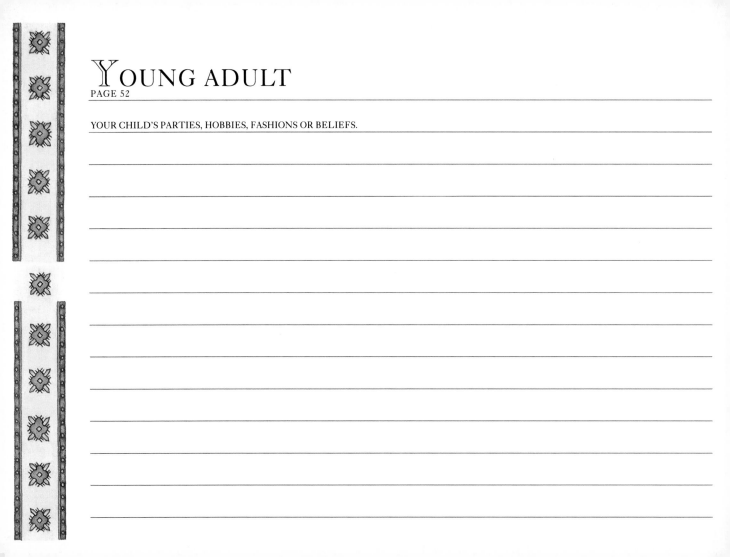

Young adult

YOUR CHILD'S PARTIES, HOBBIES, FASHIONS OR BELIEFS.

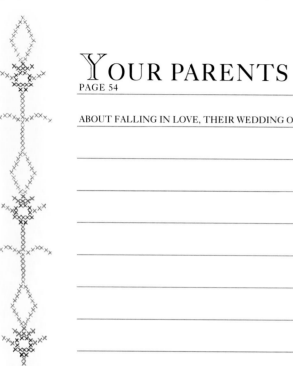

YOUR PARENTS

ABOUT FALLING IN LOVE, THEIR WEDDING OR SETTING UP HOME.

PAGE 55

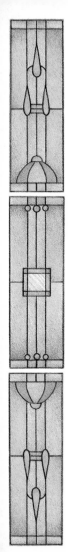

YOU!

HOW THE BIRTH OF YOUR GRANDCHILD CHANGED YOUR LIFE.

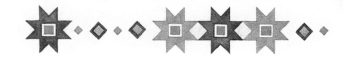

YOU: YOUR CHILDHOOD DAYS

PAGE 58

FOR SCHOOL-DAYS, PHOTOGRAPHS, EARLY WRITING OR DRAWING.

OR IT COULD BE USED FOR FRIENDSHIPS, ACHIEVEMENTS OR EARLY EVENTS.

PAGE 59

MEMORIES

IMPORTANT AND SPECIAL DAYS TO REMEMBER.

YOU AND ME

PAGE 62

FOR OUTINGS, SHARED TIMES OR THINGS YOU HAVE IN COMMON.

Me today
PAGE 64

HOW THE WORLD HAS CHANGED IN MY LIFETIME

HOW MORALS AND BELIEFS HAVE CHANGED – FROM WOMEN'S RIGHTS TO CONSERVATION.

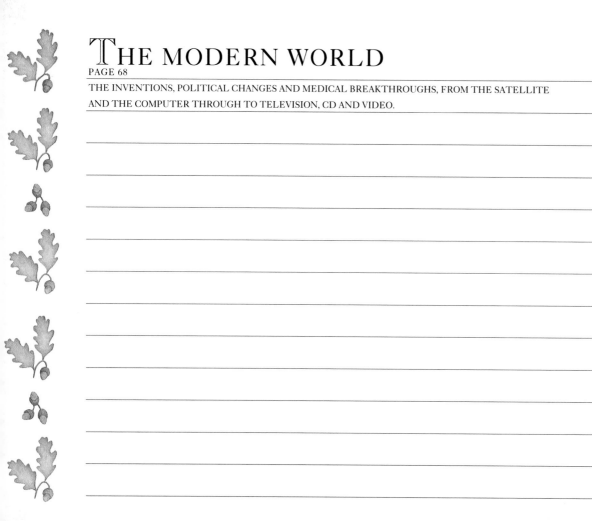

THE MODERN WORLD

PAGE 68

THE INVENTIONS, POLITICAL CHANGES AND MEDICAL BREAKTHROUGHS, FROM THE SATELLITE
AND THE COMPUTER THROUGH TO TELEVISION, CD AND VIDEO.

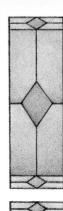

MY MOST MEMORABLE EVENTS

THE KINDEST, HAPPIEST, MOST EXCITING, SADDEST, FUNNIEST THINGS IN MY LIFE.

My SPECIAL LOVES

THE MOST-LOVED MUSIC, BOOKS, PLACES, SONGS, SHOWS OR COUNTRIES.

PEOPLE WHO HAVE CHANGED ME

FRIENDS, FAMILY, AUTHORS OR GREAT LEADERS.

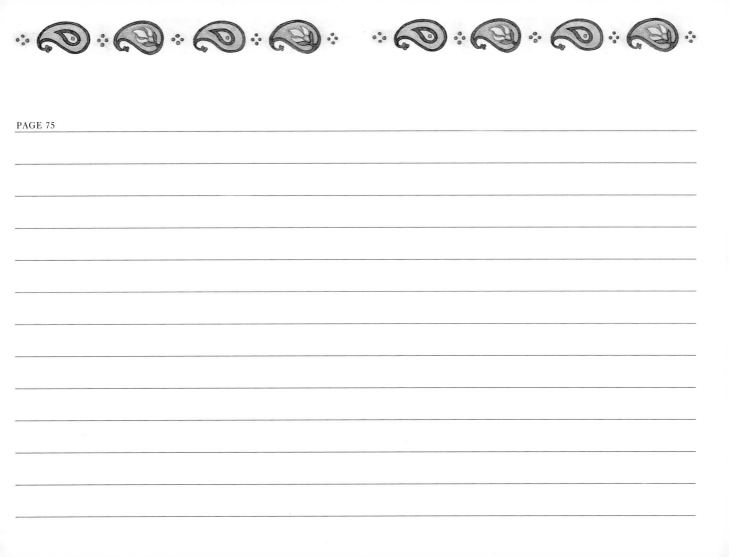

Beliefs, values, passions

FROM RELIGION TO CONSERVATION, POLITICS OR HUMAN RIGHTS.

THINGS I'D LIKE TO SHARE WITH YOU

BOOKS, SONG WORDS, QUOTATIONS AND IMPORTANT KNOWLEDGE.

PAGE 79

My wishes and hopes for you

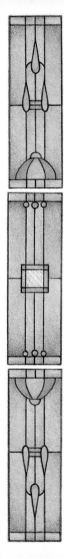

MORE SPECIAL THINGS

WE'VE LEFT EXTRA PAGES FOR IMPORTANT PERSONAL ADDITIONS, PHOTOGRAPHS
AND MEMORABILIA – ABSOLUTELY ANYTHING YOU'D LIKE TO ADD.

PAGE 84

PAGE 86

Acknowledgements

Exley Publications is very grateful to the following individuals and organizations for permission to reproduce their pictures. Whilst all reasonable efforts have been made to clear copyright and acknowledge sources and artists, Exley Publications would be happy to hear from any copyright holder who may have been omitted.

COVER: **Reifer Roggen**, W. Schtscherbakow b.1890, Archiv für Kunst.

OPPOSITE PAGE 1: **Nature**, Eliseu T. Roig (1859-1940), Museo de la Abadia, Montserrat, Catalonia, Index/The Bridgeman Art Library.

PAGE 4: **Roses**, Peter Severin Kroyer (1851-1909), The Fine Art Society, The Bridgeman Art Library.

PAGE 10: **The Herbaceous Border**, Patrick William Adam (1854-1930), by courtesy of Julian Simon, Fine Art Photographic Library.

PAGE 12: **In the Park**, Pierre Auguste Renoir (1841-1919), Private Collection, Edimedia.

PAGE 16: **The Dock at Argenteuil**, Claude Monet (1840-1926), Musée d'Orsay, Paris, The Bridgeman Art Library.

PAGE 19: **A Frugal Meal**, Frederick M. Evans (exh.1880-1916), Maidstone Museum and Art Gallery, Kent, The Bridgeman Art Library.

PAGE 23: **The Artist's Wife with their two daughters**, L. Tuxen, Skagens Museum, Denmark, The Bridgeman Art Library.

PAGE 27: **Mezzogiorno**, P. Nomellini, Private Collection, Alinari/Art Resource, New York.

PAGE 30: **Poppies**, Fred Stead b.1863, Bradford Art Galleries and Museums, The Bridgeman Art Library.

PAGE 34: **Picnic Scene**, Albert Edouard Puyplat b.1876, Waterhouse and Dodd, London, The Bridgeman Art Library.

PAGE 39: **May Morning**, © 1994, Philip Connard (1875-1958), Musée d'Orsay, Paris, The Bridgeman Art Library.

PAGE 42: **Still Life**, Claude Monet (1840-1926), Private Collection, Giraudon Art Library.

PAGE 44: **The White Tablecloth**, John Shirley-Fox (1860-1939), Private Collection, The Bridgeman Art Gallery.

PAGE 48: **The Summer Cottage**, © 1994, William Harold Dudley (1890-1949), Wolverhampton Art Gallery, Staffs., The Bridgeman Art Library.

PAGE 53: **Russian Tea**, © 1994, Irving Ramsey Wiles, National Museum of American Art.

PAGE 57: **Mother Love**, Pablio de Tommasi b.1849, Private Collection, Edimedia.

PAGE 60: © 1994 Lucy Willis, Chris Beetles Gallery, London.

PAGE 65: **Tea Under the Great Oak**, 1991, © 1994, Timothy Easton, Private Collection, The Bridgeman Art Library.

PAGE 69: **Auf der Datsche**, Konstantin Alexejewitsch Korowin (1861-1939), Tret'jakov Gallery, Moscow, Archiv für Kunst.

PAGE 72: **Meadow Flowers**, © 1994, Boris Parkhunov b.1938, Roy Miles Fine Paintings, London, The Bridgeman Art Library.

PAGE 76: **Still Life. And ever and anon the wind...**, John Edward Newton, Fine Art Photographic Library, Ltd.

PAGE 81: © 1994 Lucy Willis, Chris Beetles Gallery, London.

PAGE 85: **In the Poppy Field**, Leon Giran-Max (1827-1927), by courtesy of Galerie Berko, Fine Art Photographic Library, Ltd.

PAGE 89: **Lady in the Kitchen**, Viggo Johansen (1851-1935), Skagens Museum, Denmark, The Bridgeman Art Library.